Can you find these spring words hidden in our wordsearch?

APRIL ✓   EASTER ✓
BUDS ✓   LAMBS ✓
CHICKS ✓   MARCH ✓
CLEANING ✓   NESTS ✓
DAFFODILS ✓   SNOWDROPS ✓
DUCKLINGS ✓   TULIPS ✓

```
S V . . . . . . . .
P N . . . . . . . .
S V . . . . . . . .
H B . . . . . . . .
Q P . . . . . . R N
S M A A F R B S E A
O P I E L D O S S E
Q M A R C H T P T L
C D R E T S A E S C
D D U C K L I N G S
```

£0.99

Inside Info!

If you want to know what's where, then these two pages have all the answers.

p109

2. Spring
A puzzle and a poster all in one.

6. Fearne Cotton
One of our favourite TV girlies!

7. Rowan Lodge part 1
An elderly relative's accident leads Allie into a family mystery.

13. Room To Talk!
Find out what six readers love and hate about their bedrooms.

16. How Superstitious Are You?
We've got the answer.

17. Only A Name!
Not everyone loves Daisy's daily diary in this cool photo story.

23. We Love Dolphins!
All the info on everyone's favourite swimming superstars.

26. The Kidnap!
Why is Clara seething mad? This special prose story has all the answers.

28. Summer
It's another hot puzzle poster.

30. Staying Over
It seems like a dream come true when Lucy goes to stay with her best friend, Jane.

38. ABC Puzzles
Get out your pen and start puzzling.

40. Girls Aloud
Popsters poster.

41. The One For Me!
Paul's good-looking, smart, and the ideal boyfriend for Louise. Or is he?

p80

48. Dodgy or Divine?
What's *your* decorating style?

50. It's Fun!
Which girl has which hobby? The answers - and the pictures are all here.

51. Focus on Jennifer 1
Facts on our fave Ms Aniston.

52. Rowan Lodge part 2
Allie searches the attics, and the mystery deepens.

58. House Proud!
It's time to take a look at one of our favourite toys - the dolls' house.

60. Long Distance - it's spooky
A very strange telephone 'call' means danger for Jenny.

65. Criss-Cross!
It's the biggest and best Christmas crossword, so get busy.

66. It's Magic!
Amy fancies John, but does John fancy Amy? Find out here

68. The Write Way!
Want to be an author? Our short story writer gives you her top ten tips.

69. Sadie's Summer
There's a trip to the seaside, but no holiday, for a young Victorian servant girl.

75. Konnie Huq
A lady to light up your TV screen.

p116

p58

p6

p23

p88

p38

p118

76. Meet Me!
Sarah shares some secrets.

78. Autumn
All 'fall' down for this piggy puzzle poster.

80. Ready, Steady, Go!
Follow this fab 'n' funky flowchart to find out how fit you really are!

81. Lucky!
Gallop through this great pony tale.

88. Mystic Moggies!
Prepare to be amazed - and have a good laugh, too!

90. Spot the Differences!
The title says it all.

91. Rowan Lodge part 3
Allie goes behind the secret door - but what will she find?

97. Hilary Duff
Say hi to Hils in this hot poster.

98. Timeout! - it's spooky!
Sandy's ideal gift isn't quite what it seems to be.

103. True or False?
Test time for all fact fans.

104. Meet Me!
Now it's Caroline's turn to show us her favourite things.

106. Puzzles, Puzzles, Puzzles!
Teasers to keep your brain busy.

108. Are You Psychic or Sceptic?
Another fabby flow chart.

109. Focus on Jennifer 2
It's all the info on Ms Lopez.

110. Rowan Lodge part 4
Can Allie claim the 'treasure' and outwit her enemies?

116. Sleep Tight!
Let's look inside the bedrooms of some unusual 'babies'.

118. Best Friends?
A cool quiz for you and your buddy.

120. Secret Admirer!
Dawn turns detective when she makes a discovery in her English book.

126. Winter
Snuggle up with the final poster puzzle.

p51

Printed and published by D. C. THOMSON & CO., LTD., 185 Fleet Street, London EC4A 2HS.
© D. C. THOMSON & CO., LTD., 2006.

ISBN 1 84535 161 4

Fearne Cotton

girls! girls! girls!

Rowan Lodge

8

Hello, Auntie Mac. This is my granddaughter, Alice MacDonald Raymond. But we call her Allie.

Well, well another Alice MacDonald in the family. Just fancy that. Alice is my name, too, you see, lovey.

Oh, really?

You must be hungry. Mrs Green has put some food out for you in the dining-room.

This is awful. The bed's hard and, although everything looks clean, it smells old and musty. I hope we don't have to stay here long.

Later —

This is your room, Alice. It used to be the old nursery years ago, that's why there are bars on the window. It was to stop little children falling out.

Charming. And please call me Allie. I really don't like Alice very much.

And this place is in the middle of nowhere. It's like being in prison. I wish Mum and Dad hadn't gone to Dubai now.

The next morning, after a sleepless night in the hard bed —

This is my only brother, Cyril. He lied about his age and went to war in 1916. He was killed at Ypres after only six weeks in the trenches.

If I hear her droning on much longer I'll fall asleep. I need some air.

The girl looks just like I did at her age.

It feels really creepy looking at it. Cyril was dead good-looking, too. Maybe, if I'd had a brother, he would have looked like that?

Then things got even creepier —

What was that? It sounded like something moving in the cupboard.

Oh, it's locked. The noise must have been the water gurgling in the pipes or something.

Aaagh!

Allie. Whatever's the matter?

Nothing. I just thought I heard something in the cupboard. It's probably the central heating.

No doubt. The system is ancient. It's a lovely day, so I thought we could take Auntie Mac down to the village in her wheel chair.

11

So —

Let's go to the teashop and have a cream tea. My treat.

I'd rather just have an ice-cream, if that's okay?

All right, love. But don't wander off. Auntie Mac and I will sit by the window where you can see us.

So —

Hi, you're new round here, aren't you? I'm Kelly.

Yes. I'm Allie. I'm staying with my sort of very great aunt at Rowan Grange.

Wow, lucky you!

Why? It's a bit boring there.

Hardly. It's rumoured there's treasure hidden somewhere in the house. Lady Jane Grey stayed there once, too. You know, she was queen for nine days, and then Mary Tudor had her beheaded.

Really?

Treasure, eh? That's cool. If it's true, maybe I can try to find it. Suddenly the boring old grange has become a lot more interesting.

Continued on page 52.

12

Room to Talk!

girls! girls! girls!

We all like a good gossip with our mates, so Gabe, Leila, Abbie, Laura, Caroline and Sarah were only too happy to get together and chat about anything at all. But what we *really* wanted to hear were all the details on their own private space - their bedrooms. Read on to discover what they like, what they hate and what they'd like to change.

Do you have a room of your own, or do you have to share?

Caroline: I have my own room - thank goodness.

Sarah: Me too - and so do Gabe and Laura.

Leila: I share with my older sister, Yasmin.

Abbie: And I share with my sister, Hannah. She's only eight.

Can you describe the colour scheme at the moment?

Leila: It's sort of beige. I chose the colour myself.

Laura: Mine is pink and purple. Very girlie.

Gabe: Mine is orange, red and yellow. I chose it myself when I was younger, but now I hate it and would love to change it.

Sarah: Mine is yellow and brown. I chose it - and I still like it.

girls! girls! girls!

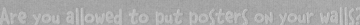

Are you allowed to put posters on your walls?

Sarah: Yes. I have lots of pictures of pop stars and actresses.
Caroline: I've got a big seal picture. I love animals.
Abbie: I'm not allowed to have things on the walls - but I'd love to. I think I'd have a mix of animals and stars.
Laura: I've got pictures of Michael Owen and me.
Gabe: I like cartoons because they're bright and cheerful.
Leila: I like singers, bands and celebrities.

Abbie

what is your favourite thing in your bedroom?

Gabe: My CD player.
Laura: My television set - and my bed. I couldn't be without that!
Abbie: All my teddies and stuffed toys and...well, everything, really.
Caroline: The chill-out area under my bed. It's a great place to escape.

what is the thing you li[ke] least about your room?

Caroline: The carpet.
Abbie: I don't like having bunk b[eds] - and I don't like having to share.
Sarah: The wallpaper. It's yellow[.]
Laura: The floor.

Do you have a TV and DVD player in your room?

Laura: Yes. I've got a video, too, so I can watch lots of different things.
Leila: I won a TV and DVD combi from the TV programme Dick & Dom in da Bungalow. I have that in my room.
Caroline: I don't have anything like that because my mum doesn't want me to have one yet.
Gabe: Yes. I like to watch funny movies and musicals.

Laura

what about music? what do you like to listen to when you're in your bedroom?

Abbie: Lemar and Kelly Clarkson.
Leila: Gwen Stephani and Green Day. Gabe likes them too.
Gabe: Yeah! And Bon Jovi.
Caroline: Lemar.
Sarah: My favourites are Hilary Duff and K T Tunstall.

what is on your window ledge right now?

Leila: A bunch of flowers.
Abbie: A snow globe and a jewellery box I got from my boyfriend.
Caroline: A hamster-shaped photo frame. I love it!
Sarah: A porcelain doll that belonged to my grandma.
Laura: Nothing! *(What? Not even dust?)*
Gabe: A Welsh dragon money box.

Caroline

Do you have a special study area in your room?

Abbie: Yes - but I don't usually work there.
Sarah: Not actually in my room. I have another room for studying in.
Gabe: I have two desks, but I usually just lie on the floor to read.
Laura: No, but I think it would be very useful if I did.

Sarah

If you could decorate your room any way you liked, what would you do?

Gabe: Blue and silver walls, a wooden floor and a white fluffy rug.
Leila: I would choose black, pink and purple paint and a pink carpet.
Sarah: I think I would have a brown rug and maybe cream walls.
Caroline: I would have a sea life theme and a wooden floor.

Leila

What do you store under your bed? Come on, be honest!

Laura: Boxes filled with all sorts of things.
Gabe: A play tent I had when I was young.
Abbie: My sister's Barbie stuff, my slippers and boxes packed with other things.
Leila: My bed has drawers underneath, so they are filled with clothes and toys.

Quickly! What do you think is the strangest thing in your bedroom?

Sarah: A big bag of clay.
Laura: My photographs.
Caroline: Fluffy, the hamster from Creature Comforts.
Leila: Me!
Gabe: My cream and medicine cupboard. It's like a pharmacy in my room. Some people collect keyrings, but I collect medication!
Abbie: All my sister's Barbie stuff.

Gabe

Finally!

The girls are all from the Newcastle area - and they certainly have plenty to say for themselves. They also all have very different hobbies which they really, really enjoy. From this list, can you guess which hobby goes with which girl? Turn to page 50 to see if you are right.

In-line skating   Boxing   Football
Disco dancing   Shopping   Horse riding

How Superstitious Are You?

Our fabby flowchart tells all!

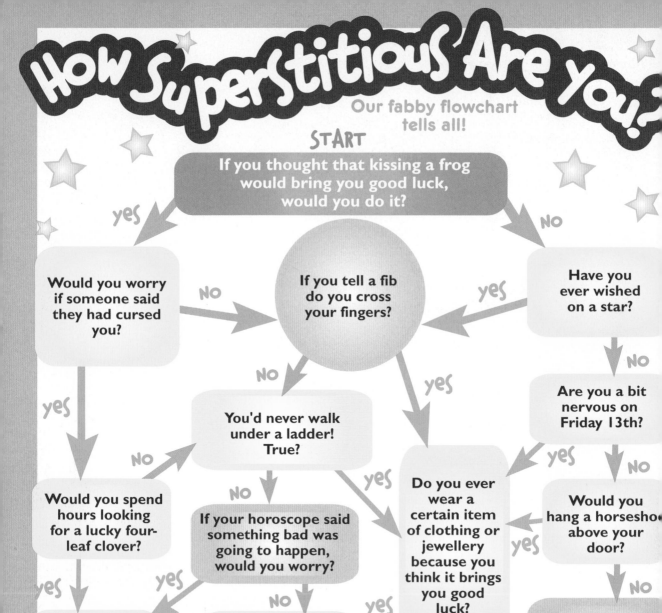

START

If you thought that kissing a frog would bring you good luck, would you do it?

yes →

NO →

Would you worry if someone said they had cursed you?

NO →

If you tell a fib do you cross your fingers?

yes ←

Have you ever wished on a star?

NO ↓

Are you a bit nervous on Friday 13th?

yes ← **NO** →

yes ↓

Would you spend hours looking for a lucky four-leaf clover?

NO →

You'd never walk under a ladder! True?

yes →

Do you ever wear a certain item of clothing or jewellery because you think it brings you good luck?

yes ←

Would you hang a horseshoe above your door?

NO ↓

NO ↓

If your horoscope said something bad was going to happen, would you worry?

yes ↓

Before an exam or competition, do you feel better if someone wishes you 'good luck'?

NO →

Do you have a dream catcher in your bedroom to catch your nightmares?

yes →

NO ↓

A black cat crosses your path. Do you think your luck will change?

NO ← **yes** →

Do you ever touch wood when you want things to go smoothly?

yes ← **NO** ↓

yes ↓

yes ↓

NO ↓

When you blow out your birthday candles, do you make a wish?

NO →

Do you carry any good luck charms?

NO →

Would you panic if you broke a mirror?

yes ↓

yes ↓

yes ←

NO ↓

Good luck, bad luck, any other kind of luck, you believe in it all. And although some superstitions can help prevent accidents, most are just fun and fairy-tale. Don't take them too seriously.

You're a modern girl, with a cool outlook - until a superstition comes along, that is. Then you're not quite so sure. But remember, Friday 13th is no different to any other day.

Miss 21st century, that's you! You know that good or bad luck depends mainly on how we behave, not crossing our fingers. But remember, the glass from that broken mirror could be dangerous.

19

Thanks, Mand. I — I feel awful. Will you walk home with me, please, Daisy? I don't want to be on my own in case I run into Sam.

Of course I will, Poppy. I'll give you a phone later, Mandy.

But what happened, Poppy? You and Sam seemed to be fine this morning.

We were — up until lunch break. Look, let's go for a Coke and I'll explain.

In the café —

You see, Sam is in the same history class as Hannah Green, and she's *always* fancied him.

So did he chuck you for her?

Oh, no! He doesn't fancy *her*. But she told him I'd been out with Ben Douglas. That's why he chucked me.

But you haven't been out with Ben, have you?

Of course not! But Hannah says she saw us together twice!

When?

20

21

we love dolphins!

Why do we smile whenever we see dolphins? Why do we feel a rush of delight when we see them leaping from the waves or playing games at sea? Maybe something tells us that the dolphin is much more than just another fish. They're funny, warm, playful and intelligent – just like us!

In fact, dolphins aren't fish at all, but warm-blooded mammals who give birth to live babies. These beautiful creatures have large brains, which make them very clever. Some scientists say they're as clever as five-year-old children, but others say they're more like young teenagers! David Holroyd, Europe's foremost dolphin trainer in the 1970s, says, "I believe that dolphins have great psychic ability." (This means that they can read your mind!) "How else could they have learned to perform such difficult tricks without the power of speech?"

Like whales, dolphins breathe through a hole in the top of their head called a blowhole. It shuts to keep out the water when they dive, and opens for air when they reach the surface. Dolphins 'speak' to each other using clicks, grunts, trills, moans and squeaks and, like us, they like to live in a family unit.

Just as we love dolphins, dolphins seem to love us! In the past, seamen escaping from sinking ships have told of dolphins carrying them to shore, and swimmers even speak of dolphins protecting them from killer sharks.

Dolphins don't sleep as we do, but bob on the surface of the sea or take small naps in the middle of a swim. They are able to do this because the two sides of their brain sleep at different times. When one half of their brain goes to sleep the other half keeps them breathing – then they swap over. While we may think all dolphins look alike, there are, in fact, 33 different types of ocean dolphin and 5 types of river dolphin known today!

If you want to know more, turn over now!

AMAZON RIVER DOLPHIN

This dolphin lives in flooded rainforests, so needs to be lithe and supple to twist in and out of the tangled tree roots and branches. This sturdy little dolphin has very small eyes and 'sees' by using sounds to build pictures in her head. She doesn't have a fin on her back, so she doesn't leap about like her ocean cousins, but still enjoys playing games and being tossed about by whirlpools. Best of all, she can change colour! Sometimes she's pink, sometimes blue-grey and sometimes off-white. That's what we call clever!

COMMON DOLPHIN

He's the most colourful dolphin with his black, grey and white skin and yellow sides. He eats plenty of fish and squid and lives in a large group. He's a super-fast swimmer and a great acrobat, both in and out of the water. He's noisy and talkative and can often be heard chattering above the surface of the sea.

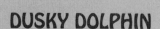

DUSKY DOLPHIN

She is the most acrobatic of all dolphins, performing some cool jumps and fancy twists! She's friendly and a bit nosy, so it's quite easy to get near to her. She moves around with hundreds of other dolphins, and even hangs around whales and sea birds!

SPOTTED DOLPHIN

You can't miss a spotted dolphin because he has — that's right, spots! He's a fast swimmer, a good acrobat and often swims close to ships. Like his cousins, he eats lots of fish and squid — and may even tuck into the odd starfish!

KILLER WHALE (ORCA)

Now, here's a shock! Did you know that the Orca is not actually a whale at all, but a dolphin? She's the largest of all dolphins, measuring over 30 feet in length, and she lives in any water, be it tropically warm or icy cold. As well as the usual diet of fish and squid, she will eat birds, seals, sharks, walruses – and even other whales and dolphins! No wonder we call her 'killer'!

BOTTLENOSE DOLPHIN

This is the dolphin we all know - the one with the friendly 'smile' who entertains visitors at marine life centres. This dolphin varies in size, depending on where she lives. Some of the world's largest bottlenoses live in UK waters! The bottlenose is an energetic, grey dolphin who likes to swim alongside ships, perform tricks and play games with her family group - which can range in size from two to 500.

RISSO'S DOLPHIN

Most dolphins have dozens of teeth in their upper and lower jaws – but this shy chappy only has a few teeth at the front of his lower jaw. He puts them to good use, however, because when playing or fighting, he nips and bites all the time – so you can always tell a Risso's because he's covered with lots of scars - just like those in our picture.

GANGES RIVER DOLPHIN

Like his Amazon cousin, the Ganges dolphin uses sound to get about because he is totally blind! He has a long beak and long, sharp teeth that show even when his mouth is closed. Instead of a fin on his back, he has a hump. He's a slow swimmer and usually likes to go around on his own or with one special friend.

There are too many other species for us to mention here, but they all have one thing in common - WE LOVE THEM!

ThE KidNAP

by Susan Elizabeth Isaacs

www.sf-illustration.com

"He'll be useful as your partner for the school disco," she continued. "No one else is likely to ask a baby like you."

□ □ □

Later, when they were on their own, Clara told her best friend, Sasha, what had happened.

"I think she's jealous of you," said Sasha.

"Jealous?" Clara was startled. "What's she got to be jealous of? She's really pretty - and she's clever, too."

"Maybe," said Sasha. "But I still think she's jealous. She wouldn't keep picking on you if she wasn't."

Clara's brother Jamie, and his friend, Oscar, caught up with the girls.

"Who's jealous?" Oscar asked with a grin. "If either of you wants to sort someone out, Jamie and I could show you some karate moves."

"No thanks," said Clara, giggling. "I may be sick of Andrea, but I still want to live."

□ □ □

CLARA'S mother always came to pick her up from school and, somehow, Andrea was always there to make some nasty comment.

"Here's Mummy come to meet her babykins," she hissed as the car pulled up.

Clara just about managed to ignore the remarks, although they really upset her, but it was the things that Andrea said about her toy rabbit, Carlos, that made Clara absolutely furious.

Carlos was a tiny fluffy white rabbit with the cutest little tail, floppiest ears, and biggest brown eyes you ever saw, and everyone who saw him loved him. He had been a present from her aunt who lived in Spain, and Clara had called him Carlos after her new baby cousin. Clara took him with her absolutely everywhere, and looked on him as her lucky mascot.

It was when she was first showing him to a group of girls that Andrea began picking on her.

"Only babies carry toy rabbits around with them," she sneered. "Do you want a rattle and bib too?" Andrea laughed at her own joke.

But things came to head on the 31st of March, which was Clara's birthday. She got exactly what she wanted from her parents – an mp3 player – and she couldn't wait to get to school to tell Sasha all about it.

She sat at her desk, opened her school bag, and prepared to take Carlos out to sit in his usual place on her desk. But he was gone!

Clara rummaged through her desk, through her coat, through her school bag. Not a sign of him anywhere. She started crawling around on the floor under her desk and, just then, a piece of paper floated down. It explained everything.

"IF YOU WANT TO SEE CARLOS AGAIN, COME TO THE OLD SHELTER AT BREAK TOMORROW MORNING. BRING MONEY!

"It's Andrea," Clara gasped as she showed Sasha the note. "I *know* it is! I'm going to see her right now, and if she doesn't give me Carlos back at once I'll...I'll…"

"You'll what?" giggled Sasha who had never seen her friend so angry. "Calm down, Clara. You don't really know it's her. It could be anybody."

"Of course it's her," said Clara. "And stop giggling. You wouldn't like it if it was your rabbit."

"Oh, come on," said Sasha grinning. "You've got to admit it's quite funny. Whoever heard of a toy rabbit being kidnapped?"

"Well, I don't care what you think," said Clara with a sniff. "I'm going to see Andrea now!" And with that she went charging off.

"How dare you take Carlos?" said Clara as she approached Andrea. "You may think it's a joke, but it's stealing – especially if you want money for him!"

Andrea's mouth dropped open, and she looked genuinely amazed.

"What on earth are you talking about? I haven't touched your stupid rabbit!"

Clara was going bright red with fury.

"Give Carlos back to me this minute. If you don't I'll…I'll… " Thoughts rushed though Clara's mind… "I'll tell your mother all about this!"

To Clara's astonishment, Andrea suddenly started to cry.

"I wish you could," she sobbed. "Mum walked out three months ago and left us all."

Clara's face crumpled with sympathy, and she reached out an arm to put round Andrea. Losing a toy rabbit was one thing, but you could hardly compare it to losing your mother.

"Oh, Andrea," she said gently as she hugged the other girl. How she wished she could say 'I'll buy you a new one'.

❑ ❑ ❑

Later that day Clara explained everything to Sasha

"Andrea *was* jealous of me," she said. "She was envious because my family seemed so happy. I've said we'll be friends from now on."

"That's great," said Sasha. "But what about Carlos?"

"Oh, gosh!" gasped Clara. "I'd totally forgotten about him. Will you come to the old shelter with me tomorrow and see what happens?"

"Sure, " said Sasha. "Just you try to stop me!"

❑ ❑ ❑

So, as soon as the break bell sounded the next morning, the two girls raced to the old shelter in the far corner of the school grounds. Would they meet the kidnapper and would they get the rabbit back?

Suddenly, two boys jumped out from behind the shelter.

"April Fool!" they shouted. It was Jamie and Oscar.

"Well done, guys," giggled Sasha. "She really fell for it!"

"You were in on this," said Clara to Sasha as the truth suddenly dawned.

"It was only a joke," said Sasha, giggling, as she disappeared with Oscar.

That left Jamie alone with Clara. He handed the toy rabbit over, and shuffled about looking a bit embarassed.

"Er – Clara. About the school disco. I was just wondering if you might like to come with me."

"I'd love to," said Clara, grinning widely. Andrea had got it wrong. Someone *had* asked her to the school disco. But she'd take Carlos along as well. Just for luck.

THE END

Summer

Can you find these summer words hidden is our wordsearch?

AUGUST PARK
BEACH PICNIC
CRICKET STRAWBERRY
HOLIDAYS SUNSHINE
ICE-CREAM SUNTAN
JULY SWIMMING

```
S H G C J U I S O I
E T R N I U U R C T
H P R E I N L E X S
O A L A T M C Y D U
L R F A W R M I H G
I K N D E B A I P U
D B E A C H E Q W A
A I M W L Q W R T S
Y O H T E K C I R C
S E N I H S N U S Y
```

Staying Over

*J*ANE DAWKINS and Lucy Gemmell were best friends. One evening, at Jane's house —

It's time you were going home, Lucy. I'll give you a lift.

So soon?

I wish we were sisters instead of best friends.

Yeah! Then we could spend *all* our time together!

For goodness sake, girls! You see plenty of each other as it is.

Then, a few days later —

We've got some news for you, Lucy. Dad's won a holiday for two. We really want to go now, so . . .

. . . we've arranged for you to go and stay with Jane.

Brilliant! Oh, I'll miss you two, but it'll be great staying with Jane for two whole weeks!

So, a few days later, Lucy moved in with Jane —

It's eleven o'clock, girls. Get to sleep or you won't be fit for school tomorrow.

Don't worry, Mum. We'll be okay.

But, next morning —

Ouch! I've knocked my leg on the end of your bed. I forgot it was there.

Yeah. Your room's a bit cramped with two beds in it.

It'll be okay if we keep it tidy. But look! You've left your things all over the floor.

You know me, Jane. I'm the original slob!

At school —

It's great having Lucy to stay. We were talking till all hours last night.

Lucky things!

At break —

Sorry I nagged this morning, Lucy. I'm just not very bright first thing.

That's okay. And I promise I'll tidy up tonight.

But —

Would you turn the light off, please? It's keeping me awake!

Tch! I'll turn it off when I finish this chapter.

Maybe!

Next morning —

I feel a bit mean about last night. I'll treat Lucy to the cinema to make up.

But —

I don't feel very well. I want to stay in bed.

You don't *look* well, I must say. I think bed's the best place for you. You'd better go downstairs, Jane.

Oh, well, I'll just go into town on my own.

And —

Hi, Jane! Where's Lucy?

She's ill, so I'm at a loose end.

I'm having some of the girls round tonight, so why don't you come? Lucy, too, if she feels up to it.

Meanwhile —

I feel *awful*. Mrs Dawkins is very nice, but I miss my own mum!

Later —

Lucy's asleep, so I can't ask if I can borrow this to go to Sue's. But I'm sure she won't mind. We always lend each other things — and I'll take good care of it.

When Jane arrived home —

Hi — are you feeling better now?

Yes — much. Did you have a nice time at Sue's?

Yeah! But everyone was asking for you and . . .

Hey! That's my new skirt you're wearing!

You were asleep so I couldn't ask. I didn't think you'd mind. After all, I've loaned you my things before.

But that skirt's new. I haven't even worn it yet.

Well no harm done. Keep your hair on. I'll take it off now.

Aaaagh!

Oh, no!

34

Look at my skirt! It's torn!

I only fell because you left your stuff on the floor, so it's your own fault.

No it isn't! You should have been more careful.

Girls! Be quiet! We can't hear ourselves think.

The girls called a truce. Then, a few days later —

That was Alan Walls on the phone! He's asked me out on Friday?

Cool!

I hope you turned him down.

No I didn't. Why should I do that?

Because you've a guest staying. You can't go out and leave Lucy alone.

It's all right, Mrs Dawkins. I don't mind.

But Mrs Dawkins insisted —

I'm sorry, Alan. I can't come on Friday. Could we make it another night?

Oh, I dunno! I-I'll be in touch!

Not! I bet I never hear from him again — thanks to Lucy.

A few days later —

Thank goodness your mum and dad come home today. I'll get my life back to normal.

And I'll get away from your nagging. I never knew you were such a pain!

Oh, Mum! It's great to see you! Did you have a good time?

Very nice — but we missed you!

Thanks for having me, Mrs Dawkins. You were very kind.

Huh! No thanks for me. Well, I don't care if I never speak to Lucy Gemmell again!

And that was the way it was!

I miss Lucy. But *I'm* not going to make up.

Then, a few days later —

I'd love to come out with you, Alan, and bowling sounds great.

My mate Lee's bringing a date, so we'll make a foursome with them.

36

But, on Friday —

Oh, no! Lee's date is Lucy. Well, I'm not going to let this spoil my evening.

I *told* you I'd be hopeless at this.

You sure did! If I'm ever up in front of a firing squad, I hope you're in it, Lucy!

I'd forgotten what a laugh Lucy can be.

Later, in the café —

. . . so old Barker *had* to let Susan eat the sweets in class!

Ha, ha, ha! I'd forgotten that story, Jane.

Do you fancy doing this again next week?

Yeah. It's been great.

Let's be friends again, Jane. I've missed you.

And I've missed you, Lucy. We were stupid to fall out the way we did.

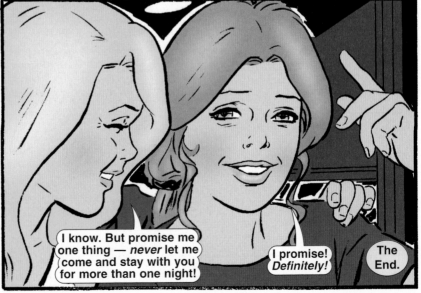

I know. But promise me one thing — *never* let me come and stay with you for more than one night!

I promise! *Definitely!*

The End.

37

a b c

How well do you know your alphabet?
Try these cool puzzles and find out.

All Square!

Can you find these names in this great worsearch? There's a girl for every letter of the alphabet.

Y	C	U	L	T	A	N	Y	A	N	Y	L
Q	T	O	O	T	Z	V	E	I	E	V	E
H	Y	L	L	E	K	C	P	V	G	O	H
A	P	P	I	L	I	H	P	I	O	N	C
N	A	D	G	R	E	T	J	L	M	N	A
N	N	Z	T	A	C	E	A	O	I	E	R
A	G	A	Q	C	S	N	N	S	N	H	U
H	E	R	C	S	E	Y	N	U	A	T	Z
B	L	A	I	L	R	W	I	N	O	N	A
Y	A	C	E	A	A	G	U	E	M	A	R
T	A	N	M	D	A	M	Q	V	I	X	I
A	L	U	S	R	U	A	Y	E	R	F	S

Angela	Beatrice
Colleen	Dawn
Elena	Freya
Gwyneth	Hannah
Imogen	Jessica
Kelly	Lucy
Mary	Naomi
Olivia	Philippa
Quinn	Rachel
Scarlett	Tanya
Ursula	Venus
Winona	Xanthe
Yvonne	Zara

Know The Score!

Simply score out all the letters that appear more than once in each square, to reveal the names of two sports.

1.

O	G	D	E
E	A	I	O
R	I	T	N
G	E	N	S

2.

A	G	B	O
T	A	C	L
B	T	A	E
F	E	C	E

Get Quizzical!

Some simple but fun questions. Each answer starts with a different letter of the alphabet, but we're not telling you which is which. We've written all the letters down, so try scoring them out as you use them. Have fun.

A B C D E F G H I J K L M N O P Q R S T U V W X Y Z

1. Hopping Australian animal
2. It goes up when the rain comes down
3. The month before May
4. Could be black, brown - or even teddy
5. Tennis player (surname) - see pic
6. The study of birds
7. Not light
8. Two days before tomorrow
9. Oval shaped food in a shell
10. The colour of the grass
11. A black and white Chinese 'bear'
12. Harry Potter's enormous friend
13. This lady's middle name - see pic
14. Cold stuff to skate on
15. A canvas shelter

16. The sign for a kiss
17. A happy sound
18. The opposite of south
19. Jewellery for fingers
20. Capital of Wales
21. Hair over your forehead
22. Stand in line
23. Goes well with ice-cream
24. Girl band - see pic
25. An animal doctor
26. Drink it from taps

Answers:

Know The Score! 1. Darts 2. Golf Get Quizzical! 1. Kangaroo 2. Umbrella 3. April 4. Bear 5. Murray 6. Ornithology 7. Dark 8. Yesterday 9. Egg 10. Green 11. Panda 12. Hagrid 13. Zeta 14. Ice 15. Tent 16. X 17. Laugh 18. North 19. Rings 20. Cardiff 21. Fringe 22. Queue 23. Jelly 24. Sugababes 25. Vet 26. Water.

Word Power! Words include: ape, bat, bath, bathe, beat, belt, bet, hat, hate, heap, help, lap, leap, pat, pal, pale, path, pea, peat, pelt, pet etc.

Girls Aloud

Girls! Girls! Girls!

THE ONE FOR ME!

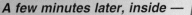

A few minutes later, inside —

What a day! Ben's ripped a cushion and dug up plants in the garden. I won't be sorry when he goes.

Oh, Mum. He's just having fun. Give him a chance. *Please!*

Don't start that again, Louise. He's going, and that's that!

Come on, Wendy. We'll get your book.

I'll work on Mum again later.

That evening —

I'm really looking forward to this date — but I'm nervous, too. I hope Paul turns up on time.

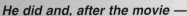

He did and, after the movie —

How do you fancy going for a pizza on Friday night? I'll come round to your place to meet you.

That'd be great, Paul. Thanks.

This has been the best evening of my life.

On Friday —

Paul's here, dead on time again. I think he's the *perfect* boyfriend.

43

44

Dodgy or Divine?

What's *your* decorating style?

Decoration isn't just for Christmas. Whether we're putting stickers on our school bags, making jewellery or covering our books, we're decorating all the time. But what does it mean? Try our fun quiz to discover what your decorating says about you!

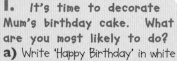

1. It's time to decorate Mum's birthday cake. What are you most likely to do?
a) Write 'Happy Birthday' in white icing.
b) Cover it with hundreds and thousands and a candle.
c) Pipe pink designs – like fairies or stars – all over it. ✓

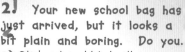

2. Your new school bag has just arrived, but it looks a bit plain and boring. Do you.
a) Stick a typed label with your name and address on it? That way you're not likely to lose it.
b) Spray silver and gold glitter on it so it stands out? ✓
c) Draw little pictures of your classmates all over the front?

3. It's your birthday party and you've decided to have a disco. But the big question is, what should you wear?
a) Jeans and a t-shirt. You want it to be casual.
b) Your Spanish dancer outfit. It is *your* party after all.
c) A pretty dress, with hand made daisy chains in your hair. ✓

4. Your mother says you ca choose the curtains and carpet for your bedroom. Wha colour scheme do you choose?
a) A simple brown carpet and cream walls.
b) Curtains with a gold trim and gol stars on them, and a carpet to matc
c) Pink carpet and curtains – with matching rose-coloured lampshades and bedspread too. ✓

5. You're decorating the Christmas tree all by yourself. Do you...

a) Choose green and red decorations? You like the traditional look.

b) Dig out the decoration box and cover the tree with every single thing you can find. ✓

c) Make your own decorations from threaded popcorn and dried fruit?

6. You're in charge of choosing and folding the napkins for a big celebration dinner. Which would you be most likely to choose?

a) White squares, folded neatly into triangles.

b) Gold threaded napkins, in silver napkin rings.

c) Something colourful, with a happy design round the border, placed in glasses. ✓

7. You have a part of the garden that is your very own. What do you grow?

a) Runner beans and carrots. They'll look nice and taste fabby.

b) Sunflowers! You think they're cool!

c) Sweet scented roses or carnations.

8. You're making a card for your best friend's birthday. What decorations do you choose?

a) White or pale coloured card with gold, stick-on letters.

b) Silver or gold card and contrasting silver or gold stars. ✓

c) Natural coloured card with dried flowers or grasses.

9. You can only afford one accessory with your birthday money. Which would you be most likely to buy?

a) A broad belt with a funky buckle. It'll go well with your jeans. ✓

b) A pack with a selection of glitzy hair accessories and ribbons.

c) A flowing scarf that you can wear to the school disco.

10. You're given some brand new school textbooks and your teacher suggests you cover them. Do you...

a) Choose a clear plastic cover so you can always see which book is which?

b) Find some glow in the dark wrapping paper and cover all your books in that?

c) Select a whole range of pink and purple tissue papers which blend beautifully with your purple school bag. ✓

Mostly a
Miss Practical
You are not a girl who likes to daydream or live in a make-believe world. You've got both feet firmly planted on the ground and know just what to do in a crisis. That doesn't make you dull, though. You may be dependable, but you're also fun!

Mostly b
Miss Glitz
You're a boogie baby, ready to dance the night away in a cloud of sparkly glitter and glitz. You're not a girl to go on a five mile country walk in your hiking boots and raincoat, but anyone who wants a life-style filled with fizz find you fabby.

Mostly c
Miss Dreamy
Your path is strewn with hearts and flowers, and romantic thoughts are never far away. You're so wrapped up in your dream world that you forget where you've put your alarm clock, or your school bag. But do you care? Not a lot.

girls! girls! girls!

It's Fun!

It's time to come clean and tell you which of our girls enjoys which hobby. Did you get them right?

▲ Gabe gets groovy on her in-line skates. She's a super speedster!

Caroline is fanatical about football. She's even got her name on the back of her shirt.

There's loadsa glitter eve— time **Laura** takes the floc— for her disco dancing.

Sarah's at home in the saddle when she goes horse riding.

▲ Who'd have guessed that angelic **Abbie** is a boxing babe in her spare time?

Our **Leila's** a label-loving laydee who just *adores* shopping! ▶

And Sarah shares more secrets on page 76.

50

focus on...
Jennifer

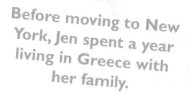

Jen's full name is Jennifer Joanna Aniston and she was born on the 11th February, 1969, in Sherman Oaks California.

She first appeared on US TV in a programme called 'Molloy' in 1990.

When she was 11, Jennifer had a painting displayed in the Metropolitan Museum of Art, New York.

At high school, Jen was known as the class clown.

Before moving to New York, Jen spent a year living in Greece with her family.

Jennifer married actor Brad Pitt in July, 2000, but was divorced in October 2005.

Jennifer has a fear of flying.

Jennifer is 1.68m tall.

Although best known for her role as Rachel in the long running 'Friends', Jen has appeared in many other hit films.

Jen was originally asked to audition for the part of Monica in 'Friends', but she refused, holding out for Rachel.

The original Greek family name was Anastassakis. Jen's father changed it when he settled in America.

Like Rachel, Jennifer has worked as a waitress.

Her fave food is Mexican but, despite being half Greek, she doesn't like Greek grub. She's not too keen on Indian or Chinese, either.

Jennifer attended the Fiorella La Guardia School of Music and Performing Arts in New York. She graduated in 1987.

Continued from page 12.

Rowan Lodge

Part 2

Huh! Well don't you go making any mess up there.

I won't!

What's *her* problem? It's an attic, after all. They're not *supposed* to be tidy.

Perhaps there's something belonging to Lady Jane Grey here. A necklace or something. That would be really valuable.

There's certainly plenty dust — but everything just looks like a load of old junk.

But —

But then —

Wow! Is this a portrait of Lady Jane Grey?

'Alice on her fourth birthday at the Elizabethan pageant. Painted by her father July 30th 1910.' Huh! It's just a portrait of a young Auntie Mac dressed up.

53

54

And don't forget to wipe your feet before you come down. This place is filthy and I don't want dust all over my carpets.

Her carpets. Huh! Mrs Green seems to think she's totally in charge at Rowan Grange. Well, we'll see about that later.

After tea Allie went for a wander in the garden —

The reason for the diary page being in the trunk is really bugging me. But I'd better not ask Auntie Mac just in case it upsets her.

Hang about, there's someone in the attic. Who on earth is it? I'd better check if the key is missing.

But —

Careful, young lady. Where's the fire?

Sorry. I — er — just wanted to see if I put the attic key back in the right place.

All present and correct. Now run along, dear. I want to mop the kitchen floor before I go home.

Oh! Right!

It must have been a trick of the light. Unless . . .

Cyril went to war in 1916. I wonder . . .

Allie told Kelly about the figure in the attic and the banging in the cupboard —

. . . so I'm beginning to think the house might be haunted, too.

Actually, I didn't like to say anything before, but the word around the village is that Rowan Grange *has* a ghost.

Really? Who is it?

But *I'm* sleeping in the nursery. The secret room must be on the other side of the cupboard door. That's where I heard the noises.

Then I'd stay well away from it, if I were you. I've heard it's not a friendly ghost.

No idea! But the ghost is supposed to make noises in some secret room near the old nursery.

Yeah, like I *can* just forget it. The first thing I'm going to do when I get back is find that missing cupboard door key.

The door's locked anyway, and there's no key. So there's no way I can go in there.

I'd keep it that way if I were you, Allie. And just try to forget about it.

Continued on page 91.

House

Girls from three to ninetythree love dolls' houses. Whether they are fully furnished in the latest style, empty shells waiting to be filled and decorated, or well loved toys, there is hardly a girl anywhere who hasn't owned, or longed to own, a house at some time in her life. So if you'd like to know more about this cool hobby, then read on.

While furnishing or creating dolls' houses as a hobby is a reasonably modern idea, the houses themselves have been around for centuries. In fact, the first record of dolls' houses can be traced back to fifeteenth century Europe. Then the little houses were also known as baby houses and were usually replicas of homes belonging to the wealthy. These houses were often decorated in exactly the same style as the real house and were used as a way of showing off. Later, similar houses were built inside cupboards or cabinets - which is how the idea of front opening houses was born.

By Victorian times dolls' houses had become recognised as playthings and, in wealthy homes, most nurseries had at least one large house for the children to play with. These houses were usually furnished to reflect the fashions of the times and, although still rather grand, were more like the houses we know today.

Traditional houses come in all shapes and sizes.

For a rustic look, you can make some furniture yourself.

Proud!

Probably the best know dolls' house of all is Queen Mary's house which was built in the early 20th century. This amazing house was a gift from the king to the queen and was designed by a very well-known architect called Sir Edwin Lutyens. It was completed in time to be shown at the Empire Exhibition of 1924 and people came from miles around to view it and be amazed at the wonderful array of miniatures which furnished the royal house. Queen Mary's house is still on display today, but now it can be found at Windsor Castle.

This 'house' has a shop below and a flat up above.

Furnishing and decorating dolls' houses is now a popular hobby and, although the basic house can cost quite a bit, decorating it needn't be all that expensive. It's true that you can go along to a specialist shop or pick up a catalogue and buy just about anything you want, but you can also make lots of things which cost next to nothing - except a bit of imagination, that is. Wrapping paper with a small pattern makes ideal wallpaper, and scraps of old material and lace make great curtains. Furniture can also be made from painted or covered cardboard or blocks of balsa wood - and strips of wood-effect sticky backed plastic makes great floor boards.

So you see, a dolls' house doesn't have to be top of the range to be fun. Sometimes a couple of shoe boxes stuck together can give just as much pleasure as a fully furnished mansion - especially if it's all yours.

You can buy ready made furniture for every room in the house.

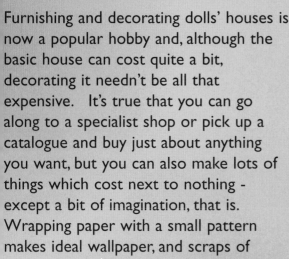

Even the bathroom!

Very funny! I suppose that was your idea of a joke, Brian, playing a fake message over the old phone.

Not guilty, Jen. There's no way a message could be played through that — and it isn't even fixed up to ring, yet.

I — I thought somebody was talking about Bleriot flying the Channel. It sounded like a young woman's voice.

Bleriot? That was in 1909! You're the one who's playing jokes, Jen.

Later —

Well, that's the set finished — all ready for the dress rehearsal tomorrow. Let's all go for a coffee.

Good idea, Brian.

Ooops! I've left my gloves in the hall. I'll catch up with you later.

Okay. See you.

The old telephone! It's definitely ringing this time!

63

CRISS-CROSS!

The biggest and best Christmas crossword around - and it's all for you.

Across:

1. A plant to hang near a hunky guy (9)
7. Here and now - or a gift (7)
8. The colour of *real* Christmas trees (5)
9. Practical presents are ones you can --- (3)
12. A Chrismas play - like Cinderella (9)
13. The number of turtle doves in the song (3)
15. Are you dreaming of this colour Christmas? (5)
18. You need to write one of these for 10 Down (4)
20. It's found inside 32 Across (8)
23. Christmas dinner is usually this (5)
25. "Ho, ho, --" says Santa (2)
27. Play these at parties (5)
28. December 24th (9, 3)
31. Look here for the star (3)
32. A Christmas bird to 'gobble' (6)
35. There's sometimes money hidden -- the pudding (2)
36. The old woman who's usually a man in 12 Across (4)
37. A seasonal song (5)
39. You may find a joke, a gift and a paper hat inside (7)
41. And 44 Across. December 26th (6, 3)
43. The colour of 40 Down's nose (3)
44. See 41 Across
45. Christmas bells do this (4)
47. Exclamation of surprise (2)
49. This puzzle is a ---- of your Christmas knowledge (4)
51. Want to add something to your Christmas list? (2)
52. And 22 Down and 1 Down. Gifts brought by the wise men (4, 12, 5)
53. Trees can be ---- or artificial (4)
55. The song says there are this many days of Christmas (6)
56. We all eat too ---- at this time of year (4)
57. And 50 Down. You may take one of these to buy presents (8, 4)

Down:

1. See 52 Across
2. It glitters on the tree (6)
3. We can't wait to do this to our presents (4)
4. The main decoration (4)
5. You can relax once all your cards are this (4)
6. Cold, fluffy stuff that turns the ground white (4)
9. Bet you get -- extra early on Christmas morning (2)
10. And 37 Down. Cuddly chap who brings gifts (5, 5)
11. Do this under 1 Across (4)
14. The season for Christmas (6)
15. Turkey leftover that can be pulled for luck (8)
16. Weather to make you slip (3)
17. "Star -- wonder, star -- night…" (2)
19. -- Nicolas - another name for 10 Down (2)
21. Number of wise men (5)
22. See 52 Across.
24. Will we say this if offered second helpings? (3)
26. There are usually lots of these with 32 Across (9)
28. We usually send one to each of our friends (4)
29. All we'll want to do after eating too much (3)
30. You may not get any presents if you don't do this (3)
33. It's traditionally burned at Christmas (4, 3)
34. Found in a pear tree, we're told (9)
35. Do this to decorate a cake (3)
37. See 10 Down
38. We may ask for either this -- that (2)
40. The most famous reindeer (7)
41. Cinderella's friend - or chocolate (7)
42. A shortened form of Christmas (4)
46. Invite your friends to this (5)
48. A prickly plant that goes with ivy (5)
50. See 57 Across
51. A good ---- should make sure everything goes well (4)
54. What we hope you have lots of (3)

Answers on page 107.

It's Magic!

by Tracy Joy Holroyd

AMY saw the bike approaching in the distance and straightened so she could see over the fence. As the bike passed, she flashed her brightest smile and hoped.

The boy on the bike stared steadily ahead, pedalled furiously and, within moments, disappeared around the corner.

Amy's shoulders slumped. John Conner rode by her house at the same time every Saturday. For the last three Saturdays, she had made sure she was working in the garden, hoping he'd notice her and stop. But he never did.

She wandered to the fence and absently stroked the silky head of her black cat, Wush.

"Oh, Wush!" she sighed. "Same again. Nothing. Not even a glance. If I don't get to meet him soon, he'll find some other girl and I'll stand no chance. I'd cast a spell on him if I could, but…" suddenly, she stopped! "Hey, what about that book of fun spells Mum bought me for my birthday? I wonder if there are any love charms in that!" She stared at Wush thoughtfully. "Would you help me, Wush, if you could?"

Wush regarded her

steadily with unblinking, golden eyes.

★ ★ ★

That night, Amy sat on a bench in the back garden and laid out her tools – lavender water, a mirror and Wush's brush. She shivered in the late autumn breeze and glanced up at the full moon.

"It should be a May moon, really," she explained to Wush, "but this will have to do. At least the moon's full. "Now, I need you on my knee," she told the cat.

As if he understood, Wush took his nose out of the lavender water, jumped on to

Amy's lap and curled up.

Smiling slightly, Amy sprinkled his coat with lavender water, picked up his brush and started to groom him. As she brushed, she whispered the words writtten in the book.

Then Amy brushed and brushed and brushed until Wush's fragrant coat gleamed in the moonlight. After she'd finished brushing, she lifted the mirror to his face and showed him his reflection.

"Aren't you the most handsome one?" she asked him.

He purred.

⭐ ⭐ ⭐

The following Saturday, a deep frost had fallen overnight. Brown leaves crunched under Amy's feet and glassy pools of iced water glittered on the pathway and the road.

Amy couldn't imagine that John Conner would be out today – the roads were far too slippy for cycling. And she couldn't think what to do in the garden. The ground was too hard to dig. The leaves were too stiff to sweep.

"What do you think, Wush?" Amy asked the cat as he rubbed against her leg. "Not much chance of John being out today, huh?"

Wush skipped playfully away from her, then leapt lightly on to the gate. Except for a flicking tail, he sat very still, staring up the road.

Then, suddenly, Amy saw the familiar figure of John Conner wheeling his bicycle out of his front gate and on to the road.

"He's coming, Wush!" Amy whispered. Quickly, she pushed her hair away from her face and edged towards the gate. She stepped on to the path, then bent over the gate and pretended to be working on the latch.

She could hear the wheels of the bike approaching and she glanced up slyly.

The bike wasn't travelling as quickly as usual, but it was still too quick to be safe in the icy weather,

"Oh, no!" Amy thought. He's going to do it again – he's going to ride straight past me!

Like a streak of lightning, Wush shot off the gate and across the road - directly in front of the bicycle.

John Conner's eyes widened, his mouth fell open and he swerved, causing his bike to fly straight into the little hedge outside Amy's garden!

As Amy raced out, Wush strolled back, as if to see what was going on.

"I'm so sorry," Amy cried, suddenly realising that John might be hurt. "I don't know what made him do that. Are you okay?"

John looked down at his bike, which seemed to be none the worse for its detour.

"Yeah! He said angrily. "No thanks to your stupid cat."

"You must be shocked, though," said Amy. "You'd better come inside and Mum will make you a hot drink."

"No, no," John insisted. Then he looked at Amy for the first time - and his angry expression melted. "Er - well, on second thoughts…" he stuttered. "If you don't mind?"

⭐ ⭐ ⭐

Inside the warm kitchen, Amy and John sat drinking hot chocolate as Wush watched from a nearby chair.

"I'm really, *really* sorry," Amy repeated for the hundredth time. "I don't know what made Wush dive out like that. He's never done it before."

"Please don't apologise," John smiled shyly. "It's given me a chance to speak to you. I've wanted to for ages, but I didn't know what to say." John blushed as he held out his mug for a refill of chocolate.

"You know the really strange thing?" John suddenly added, thoughtfully. "I noticed your cat watching me as I was riding down the road. If I didn't know better, I'd think he ran in front of me on purpose."

"Oh, Wush would never do a thing like that!" Amy insisted, rubbing the cat's silky head. Then, smiling softly, she whispered into Wush's pricked ear, "Unless, of course, he had a very good reason…"

⭐ *The End*

The Write Way!

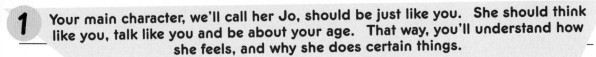

Would you like to write a story like the one you've just read? If you would, then our author, Tracy, has a few tips to set you on your way to becoming a top short story writer.

1 Your main character, we'll call her Jo, should be just like you. She should think like you, talk like you and be about your age. That way, you'll understand how she feels, and why she does certain things.

2 Give Jo a problem. Is she being bullied? Is she jealous of a sister? Maybe someone else has the problem and Jo wants to help them. Perhaps she knows a lonely old woman who needs company. If Jo doesn't have a problem, *you* don't have a story!

3 Introduce Jo and her problem right at the beginning of your story. The reader doesn't really want to know that it was a sunny morning when Jo got up, washed her face, cleaned her teeth and combed her hair. That's not exciting – that's boring! Yawn!

4 Use plenty of dialogue and lots of action. That means plenty of chatter and people doing things – vacuuming the house, struggling with a maths paper, eating ice-cream.

5 Try to draw pictures with your words. If Jo is unhappy, don't just say, 'Jo was unhappy'. Instead, say something like, 'Jo slumped to her knees, hot tears spilling down her cheeks'.

6 Once you've set the exciting opening scene, tell the reader how Jo got into the mess in the first place! Perhaps her kid sister did something that landed Jo in trouble with her parents. Jo not only feels hurt, she also hates her sister! This is called a backflash and should only take a couple of lines.

7 As you carry on with your story, split it into scenes – like in a film or TV programme. End each scene at an exciting point, so we will want to read on. If you don't, we might just fall asleep!

8 Build all your scenes into one climax – a point where things can't get any worse, exciting, or terrifying! Perhaps Jo is struggling at the edge of a cliff, trying to pull the sister she hates to safety! She heaves her sister upwards, sliding through the mud until she feels sick and dizzy. Her pale face is filthy and her fingers are bleeding! That's action!

9 End your story happily. Let Jo solve her problem and learn something at the same time. She rescues her sister and suddenly realises just how much she loves her. The ending should only take one or two lines and, as you can see, neatly solves Jo's problem. How can you feel jealous of someone you love.

10 Finally, tell your story in as few words as possible. Make sure the words you use are good words - like ambled, strolled or sauntered intead of walked slowly. And don't repeat yourself. There's no need to say someone was tired *and* weary, because both words mean the same thing.

Follow these simple rules - and have fun!

Sadie's Summer

TWELVE-year-old Sadie Waters was the youngest maid in Mr and Mrs Taviston's Victorian household. One hot day in July, Sadie was hard at work —

Get a move on, girl! There's a load more washing still to be done.

It's so hot in here, Mrs Griggs. Can't I sit down for a second?

Oooh! Look at all the beach huts. This is the most exciting day of my life. I'm going to go down to the beach on my very first day off.

But —

All servants' holidays are cancelled while we're here.

Oh — but I wanted to go to the beach!

Well that's the master's orders. Now get on with scrubbing that floor!

It doesn't seem fair. We're so close to the sea, but we can't enjoy it.

A few days later —

The mistress is in a right mood today. Oh, no! She's ringing again!

Go and see what she wants, Sadie.

I want *all* my gloves washed — and don't damage them!

I'll be very careful, Ma'am.

Soon —

There! They're sparkling white!

Hang them on the line, then. And don't dally. I've other chores for you to do.

I can smell the sea from here. Oh, if only I could spend even a few hours on the shore.

71

Suddenly —

Oh! Where did *you* come from?

I'd better get that glove back. He might tear it!

Here, boy! Give me that glove!

Got it!

Well done! You've caught Monty!

Who?

Monty. His real name's Montague Marchmont the Third, but I call him Monty for short. He's a sweet little thing, but he keeps running off. I can't control him.

Thank you so much for catching him for me.

It was nothing. I really just wanted to get my mistress's glove back.

Oh, no! It's torn!

You must let me give you a reward.

If — if you could tell my mistress that it was your dog that tore this glove and not me, I'd be very grateful.

72

Of course I will! But you deserve more than that. What else would you like?

I'd really like a day at the beach — but my master won't allow that.

The Honourable Sarah White has called to ask if we can allow you a day off. It's very tiresome, but her father is a member of the House of Lords, so we shall have to agree.

Wonderful!

So, outside —

Jump in, Sadie! We're going to the beach!

How lovely! I can hardly believe this is happening!

Soon —

The pierrots are so funny! *You* like them too, don't you, Monty?

Ouch! The water's freezing! Someone ought to heat it up!

Later —

Oh, dear — it's time to go home. I almost wish I hadn't come now.

Why? Haven't you enjoyed it?

73

girls! girls! girls!

Konnie Huq

Hi, my name is sarah and I'd like you to come inside my house so I can show you a few of my favourite things!

This is my Bear Factory bear. She has lots of different outfits, so I made her a wardrobe out of a cardboard box. Cool, eh?

I loved the TV show 'Friends', so Mam and Dad bought me the whole first series on DVD. I watch them over and over again.

Budgie is hiding behind his mirror because he is a little sad and shy at the moment. He belonged to my grandad who died, and we're both still missing him. Grandad called him Bonnie Lad.

This cool manicure set was a present. It's fun to use and it helps me keep my nails looking nice.

Meet Minnie Mouse. I just adore her spotty skirt and bow. My friend, Caroline, has one too.

My dog Mollie likes to come up and jump on my bed. We put a baby gate on the stair to stop her coming up, but she still manages it somehow.

I have a collection of dolls which were presents from other countries. I like my Miss Scotland and Miss Wales best. Miss Wales is a little bit bald because I used to play with her hair. It's just as well she wears a hat.

This is my favourite outfit. I always feel good when I wear it.

I have two rabbits and some guinea pigs. The rabbits are quite hard to catch and live mostly in the garden. They are both really lively - and very heavy.

When my dad went to Disneyland with some of his students, he brought me this Tigger. It's my favourite soft toy at the moment.

She isn't my favourite singer, but I liked the poster and thought it would brighten up my wall.

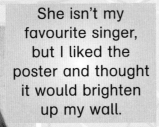

Finally, my big secret. I just *love* playing the piano - but not in front of anyone.

catch up with caroline on page 104.

Autumn

Can you find these autumn words hidden is our wordsearch?

APPLES	OCTOBER
BROWN	PUMPKIN
FUN	SCHOOL
HALLOWE'EN	SEPTEMBER
LEAVES	SPARKLERS
NOVEMBER	WIND

```
N A P P L E S X W R
O E M U X D L E S E
C D E S M E H R B B
T N P W A P E D A M
O I W V O L K I F E
B W E O K L J I U T
E S Z R R T L Q N P
R F A W K B X A Y E
N P L O O H C S H S
S N O V E M B E R A
```

Ready, Steady, Go!

Try this fun fitness flowchart.

START

Do you love games at school?

Is going to the cinema one of your favourite hobbies?

Are you in a sports team?

You like to read a lot. True?

Do you sometimes spend hours on your hair and make up?

Casual clothes are your favourites. True?

Do you have a big collection of DVDs or videos?

You don't like getting hot and sweaty. True?

Have you ever recorded a TV sport programme to watch later?

Everyone says you have lots of energy. True?

Shopping is your favourite way to spend a Saturday. True?

Would you like to go on an adventure holiday?

At a party, you're always first on the dance floor. True?

Do you know what a sports field is? It would be fair to say that you don't put sport at the top of your 'must do' list. But a little exercise *is* good for you, so you should try to get out and about a bit more.

You're quite keen on sport, and enjoy getting out and about with your mates. You don't take it too seriously though, as you see sport and exercise as fun - and like watching just as much as taking part.

Wow! Miss Super-fit, that's you. We're surprised you actually had time to do this flowchart. But, while exercise *is* good for us, we don't have to be on the go *all* the time. It's good to sit back and relax at times, too.

Lucky!

LISA BLAKE, whose parents ran a boarding stables, had her own pony called Lucky. Her friend, Jodi, kept her pony with the Blakes, and the two girls loved going for long gallops over the moors —

Come on, Lisa. We're going to beat you

Whoa, Lucky. Oh, sorry, Maxwell. We didn't see you coming.

No wonder you two don't win any big competitions — you're always mucking about.

But we like riding for fun. You never seem to do that.

Well, I've been invited to represent Britain at a European 'Rural Riders' camp. I call *that* fun!

Wow! That *is* great. Well done, Maxwell.

Yeah! I hope you do well.

But, when Lisa arrived home —

I don't believe it! Lucky and I have been invited to the camp, too, because we came second in that 'Top Rider' class a few months ago.

You lucky thing!

Well done, Lisa. Let's have a look at all the details.

One person wasn't too pleased —

Trying to smarten him up for the trip, are you? I wouldn't bother! You can't improve a plain cob like him.

Lucky isn't plain — he's just like all registered Welsh Cobs. Look, Maxwell, we're going on this trip together, so let's at least *try* to get on?

Of course. I'm certainly not going to let you spoil my trip. Besides, we'll probably be in totally different groups.

We can but hope, Maxwell.

At last it was time to go —

I'm glad your pony's a good loader, Lisa. One of the others caused quite a hold up. She didn't like the lorry at all.

Lucky's always pretty sensible, Mrs North.

'Bye, Lisa — and enjoy yourself!

I will, Dad. 'Bye, Mum! 'Bye, Jodi.

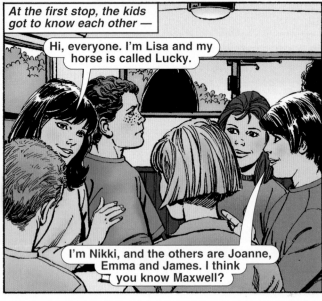

At the first stop, the kids got to know each other —

Hi, everyone. I'm Lisa and my horse is called Lucky.

I'm Nikki, and the others are Joanne, Emma and James. I think you know Maxwell?

Suddenly —

Oh, what was that thud?

One of the horses, of course. I hope Midnight's okay.

It's Starlight, I think. But we'd better check them all out.

I hope Starlight isn't upsetting Midnight.

What a pain Maxwell is.

Maybe we should put Lucky in with Starlight, Mrs North. He's very good with nervous horses.

Good idea, Lisa. It's certainly worth a try.

See? He's trying to tell her it's all right.

It really looks as if he is.

And, later —

She's eating her hay now. She's fine again — thanks to you and Lucky, Lisa.

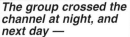

The group crossed the channel at night, and next day —

Mrs North says there will be lessons, picnic rides, cross-country rides and a competition.

Midnight and I will really only be interested in the competition. A European rosette would look good on my board at home.

Maxwell, can't you just relax and have a good time?

This way, please. Stables have been reserved for your horses.

What a great place. it's a proper Equestrian Centre.

I'm glad Lucky is next to Starlight. Having him near will keep her relaxed.

I like Midnight in the end box. I don't want people giving him tit-bits or patting him all the time.

Later —

Get tidied up, girls. Dinner is at eight o'clock in the members' restaurant.

Ohhh! That sounds a bit posh!

It was —

I hope I don't spill my soup or use the wrong knife or fork.

Really, Lisa! Don't you know *anything*?

Get real, Maxwell — she's only joking!

Yeah! I'm sure I'll manage without your help.

He really thinks he's something! If he does well when we start riding, he'll be unbearable.

And —

You have a very nice horse, Maxwell. He works well.

I can almost see Maxwell's head swelling. But Midnight *is* good at dressage and most other things.

Later —

We will be given marks each day for performance and effort. At the end of the week, there will be a trophy for the best rider. I think your Maxwell may win.

If there's a trophy to be won, Maxwell will certainly go all out to get it, Brigit!

Most of the horses went well, but —

Someone needs to give Socks a lead. Maxwell, you go first.

That's it. Now wait in the water, Maxwell. When Socks sees you, it'll give him confidence.

But Maxwell didn't stop. So —

Lucky will show it's safe. Just follow us. We'll wait for you, Joanne.

Good boy, Lucky. Socks is starting to follow. He trusts you — just like the other ponies do.

Well done!

Good boy, Socks!

At last! Can the rest of us get on now?

Just ignore him, Joanne. Maxwell thinks he's more important than anyone else.

And, at the end of the course —

Well done, Maxwell. That was the best round of the day.

You went well too, Lucky, but your legs are too short for you to be as fast as Midnight. But we did our best.

That afternoon —

Can someone go forward and open this gate?

I'll do it. My horse is very obedient.

So is Lucky, but I suppose Maxwell's after more marks for the trophy.

Later, there was a barbecue —

Tomorrow we begin with an inspection of your turn-out, then there will be dressage.

Early next morning —

I've really polished you and your tack, Lucky. I just hope the rain doesn't spoil everything.

It did, but —

That bag startled her — and it looks as if she's going to throw Nikki.

Starlight! Whoa, girl!

Sure enough —

Come on, Lucky!

Someone stop her! She'll get on to the road.

We're coming, Starlight. That's right, Lucky — you call to her as well.

Good girl. Stand now.

Thanks, Lisa. But I think we'll have to drop out of the turn-out inspection. Starlight is covered in mud — and so are you and Lucky.

At the dressage —

Maxwell will definitely be top at this, Lucky, but never mind.

And —

Maxwell looks so smug! But I've had a great time — even if I haven't won anything.

Later, in the stables —

Midnight's stall is empty. Where's Maxwell gone?

I bet he's out on the cross-country course.

It'll be dark soon, so I'm going to look for him. If we aren't back in an hour, raise the alarm.

I will. Be careful, Lisa.

Lucky seemed to know where he was going, and —

Lisa! Midnight's stuck! He slipped off the bank. I can't hold his head much longer.

I'm coming! Quick, Lucky!

Tie that to Midnight's girth. Lucky will keep his head up and pull.

It worked.

That's it, Lucky. Keep going!

Thank you, Lisa! You saved his life!

Back at the camp —

He seems all right now. He's warm and isn't shivering.

Thank goodness he wasn't hurt. But we'd better go or we'll be late for the farewell dinner and the presentation of the trophy.

They made it just as the winner's name was being announced —

As the trophy is for endeavour and outstanding behaviour as well as good showing in all activities, our unanimous decision is . . . Lisa Blake — the most helpful member of our camp. Along with her pony, Lucky, of course.

Well done, Lisa! You deserve it.

And so the European trip came to an end —

It was fun, Lucky, wasn't it? But it's good to be home again. The trip proved one thing though. I wouldn't change you for all the Midnights in the world!

The End.

Mystic Moggies!

Did you read the story on page 66? If you did, do you think the cat, Wush, really helped Amy to get to know John, or do you think it was just coincidence? Whether it's magic or merely mischief, many people throughout time have believed that cats possess special powers and, because of that, there are loads of myths and superstitions surrounding our favourite pet.

Cat Naps!

Have you ever had a dream about a cat? If you have, then the colour of the cat in your dream could be very important.

✳ White or black means good luck.

✳ Tortoiseshell means you will be lucky in love.

✳ If the cat is ginger, you can expect riches.

✳ A tabby cat means a happy home.

✳ If you see a grey cat, then you are a dreamer.

✳ A black and white cat means a birth in the family.

Believe it or Not!

✳ Some early American settlers believed that if a cat jumped into an empty cradle, it meant that there would soon be a birth in the family. (If there was an empty cradle lying around, it probably meant that a baby was on its way, anyway.)

✳ It was said that if a cat sneezed five times, the family would catch a cold. (Probably from the cat!) On the other hand, Italians believed that a sneezing cat brought good luck.

✳ French peasants believed that if you let a cat loose at a five-way road junction, the cat would lead you to buried treasure. (Either that, or he'd just get you lost!)

✳ Some people believed that finding a white hair on a black cat meant that good luck was on its way. (Removing it would be more likely to bring bad luck — and a good scratching!)

✳ An old Scottish belief said that a strange black cat at your door would bring prosperity. (Only if there was a reward on offer for finding it!)

✳ Long ago, when sailing ships became becalmed, sailors would lock the ship's cat in a cupboard. They believed that this would make the wind blow. (It would certainly make the cat mad!)

cat crazy!

If you thought the **Believe it or Not** section was weird, wait till you read this!

✳ In the 16th century, visitors were expected to kiss the house cat!

✳ Cats can spread gossip, so they should never be allowed to hear secrets.

✳ Witches turn into cats after dark – so avoid black cats at night.

✳ A kitten born in May will become a witch's cat!

✳ If you move house you should always put the cat in through the window rather than the door. That way he won't leave.

✳ It's bad luck to cross a stream while carrying a cat!

Weather or Not!

According to some legends, cats are world-class weather forecasters.

✳ A cat looking out a window is looking for rain.

✳ A restless cat means a storm is coming.

✳ If a cat sits with its tail towards a fire, then bad weather is on its way.

✳ If a cat claws the carpet you can expect high winds.

✳ If puss sleeps with all four paws under his body, then it is going to be cold.

✳ If your cat washes its face, but not its ears, then the weather will be good.

Finally - It's A Fact!

✳ White cats are usually deaf!

✳ Cats spend up to sixteen hours a day sleeping.

✳ A cat's heartbeat is around twice as fast as yours.

✳ Like our fingerprints, cat's nose pads are all different.

✳ Cats don't miaow at other cats.

✳ Sir Isaac Newton invented the cat flap.

Feline Fun!

✳ If you want to know the answer to an important question, sit in a quiet room with the door slightly open. Make sure your cat is in the next room. Write your question on a piece of paper, then read the question aloud. Now call your cat. As she comes through the door, watch which paw appears first. If it is the left paw, the answer to your question is no. If it is the right paw, the answer is yes. Alternatively, you could always ask your parents or a friend! It's probably a lot less bother.

✳ When you see a rainbow, call your cat to you and stroke her from head to tail three times, each time making a wish. Then wait for your wishes to come true – maybe!

✳ A stye in your eye or a wart on your hand can be cured by rubbing it three times with the tail of a cat. Always ask the cat's permission first, of course!

✳ Before you post a Valentine card, sprinkle it with rose water and get your cat to kiss it with his nose. It's said that whoever receives your card will ask you out before the end of February. If they don't, you could always try asking them out yourself!

Spot The Differences!

It's simple! There are at least 12 differences between these two christmas pictures. can you spot them? The answers are on page 107.

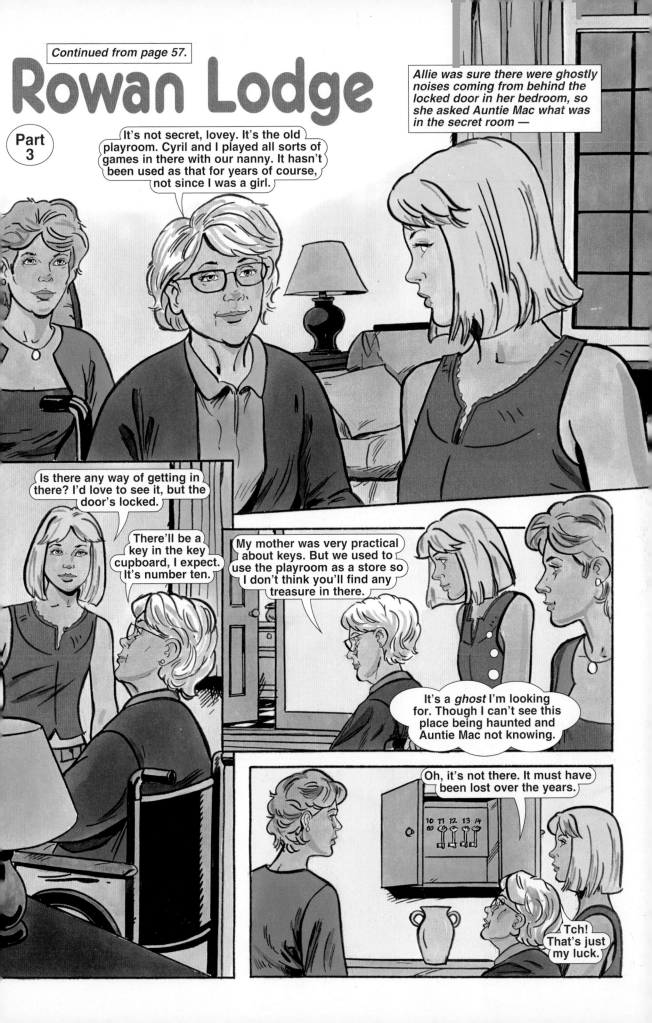

But don't the cleaners ever go in there, Auntie?

I suppose they must, dear, but I'm not sure. Mrs Green may have the key, but she won't be in till lunchtime.

But wait a minute! There's another door on the first floor, leading off the back stairs. We used to call it nanny's door as it was the one she used.

Really? I'll see if it's open.

And —

Success! But now what? Dare I go in?

Allie did —

Nothing — except a bit of a mess. But I wonder if the bang I heard was that drawer falling on to the floor?

Hang on! These are modern pens, so someone's been here recently. Perhaps it's the same person I saw in the attic.

Just then —

Someone's coming. I'd better hide.

It's Kelly from the village. What on earth is *she* doing here?

Now behave, Kelly, and don't make any noise. I don't want Miss MacDonald finding out you're here. And tidy up the mess you made yesterday.

Yes, Mum. But it wasn't *my* fault. I told you, it was as if the drawer fell out on its own.

Mum?

Oh, it's been tidied up already! What . . .

It's okay, Kelly. It was only me.

Phew, Allie. You didn't half give me a fright.

I gave *you* a fright? You nearly scared me out of my wits with your ghost stuff.

94

Sorry about that, but I didn't want you finding me. Miss MacDonald doesn't know I'm here, but I've nowhere else to go when Mum's working during the holidays.

That's okay. I'm sure Auntie Mac won't mind, especially if we say you're here to hang out with me. It'll be fun having someone my own age around.

Come on. Let's sort things out now.

Cool. Then I can help you treasure hunt.

And —

Of course you can come and see Allie, my dear. Feel free to bring your daughter any time you want, Mrs Green.

Thank you, Miss MacDonald.

Allie spent the rest of the day with Kelly —

This place is massive. The treasure could be anywhere.

Kelly keeps on about the treasure, but for some reason I don't want to show her the map I've found.

That evening —

It looks like a map of the main hall, and it says 'Ten steps to the left, then turn right and open and shut the Bible twice'. What on earth does that mean?

Allie decided to try it out —

Okay, ten steps to the left.

95

After only eight steps I'm at the wall. This can't be the right place.

Hang about, the map says Rowan *Lodge*, but this is Rowan *Grange*. Where's the lodge, then? And who are Lally and Rilly?

Allie knew just who to ask —

My goodness, what a question. That's the name Cyril and I gave to our summerhouse. We used to play there a lot, but how did you hear the name?

Er — it was on a piece of paper in the playroom.

That's not exactly a lie.

So whatever this refers to is in the summerhouse. And the names are probably nicknames — Rilly for Cyril and Lally for Alice. I bet he hid her birthday present before he went to war, but the map was lost so the gift was never found.

Unknown to Allie, she was being watched —

With luck I'll be able to find it and give it to Auntie Mac. It may not be priceless treasure, but I'm sure she'll be thrilled.

Continued on page 110.

The programme I want to see is on at six-thirty, so that's where I'll put the clock hands now.

And —

Sandy, that's your programme starting now!

It really *does* work! What a fantastic clock! Who'd be crazy enough to sell it back for five pounds?

Later —

Don't forget, Sandy — when that's over, it's homework time.

Yes, Mum.

I'm really too tired for homework tonight. Perhaps I'll try another experiment.

So, after the programme —

I'll put the hands to bedtime. I can always catch up with my homework at the weekend.

Moments later —

I haven't heard a peep from you for two hours, Sandy. But if you're finished, just go off to bed.

Okay, Dad. Goodnight.

Next morning, however, Sandy remembered something —

Oh, gosh! There's a test this morning on the homework I didn't do last night! I think I'm going to need the clock!

At school —

Now to make myself scarce for a couple of minutes, by which time it should be . . .

BOILER ROO

. . . lunch break! Neatly done, clock! Mind you, I've just had breakfast, but I'll have to try to eat something, or someone will ask questions.

DINING HALL

There was something else Sandy hadn't thought about —

Hi, Sandy! Where have you been all morning?

Yes! I'd like to know that, too. *And* why didn't you hand in your test-paper? Come to the staff room after lunch and explain yourself!

Oh, no! How do I get out of this one?

By using the clock, of course —

I'll wind it on to four o'clock so that I can do my homework tonight and — wait a minute! If I wind it on twenty-four hours, it'll be *Friday* night and I'll have the whole weekend to think up an excuse!

2006
JUN 15
THURSDAY

101

Then she caught sight of herself in a mirror —

Oh, no! I've grown up! I must have turned the drill the wrong way and I've gone ten years into the future!

2016
NOV 10
TUESDAY

Stunned, Sandy walked towards the house —

The house is a mess — *and* empty! Perhaps these people know where Mum and Dad are.

No one's lived there since Mr and Mrs Harris left. Their daughter disappeared about ten years ago. The parents never got over it. Very sad.

FOR SALE

Sandy ran back to the shed —

The clock's still going! Maybe I can put things right.

And —

Not going out again, are you, Sandy?

I won't be long, Mum. I bought an old clock, but it doesn't work properly, so I'm taking it back.

2006
WED
JUNE
14

Well, remember that your dad will be back at a quarter past five. Why is your hand bandaged, by the way?

Oh, I was trying to fix the clock, that's all.

And it takes a long, painful time to turn back a clock — by hand!

If you're a fact fan, you'll love this simple quiz. All you have to do is say which of the following statements are true, and which are false.

TRUE OR FALSE?

1 Bart Simpson is Jessica Simpson's cousin.

2 A lion's roar can be heard up to three miles away.

3 It cost £60 million to make the movie, *The Chronicles of Narnia*.

4 A sneeze leaves the mouth at up to 600mph.

5 Reese Witherspoon was born in Australia.

6 Daniel (Harry Potter) Radcliffe once played Oliver Twist.

7. *Would you buy shoes from this man?*

12. *Was he a Holby hunk?*

19. *A teenage sensation?*

7 X Factor winner, Shayne Ward, once worked in a shoe shop.

8 The oldest TV soap is Coronation Street.

9 A chameleon's tongue can be twice as long as its body.

10 A goldfish will turn white if it is kept in the dark.

11 Madonna's real name is Madonna Veronica Louisa.

12 Orlando Bloom has been in the TV programme, *Casualty*.

13 There are only 15 letters in the Hawaiian alphabet.

14 Smiling uses more muscles than frowning.

15 Keira Knightly is 1.70m (5ft 7in) tall.

16 Brad Pitt graduated with a degree in English.

17 All snowflakes are identical.

18 Rachel Stevens studied at the London School of Fashion.

19 Billie Piper topped the charts when she was just 15 years old.

20 Blue Peter first appeared on TV screens just over fifty years ago.

5. *Is she an Australian?*

Answers:

1. False (of course). 2. False. It's up to five miles away. 3. True. 4. True. 5. False. Reese was born in Baton Rouge, Louisiana, USA. 6. False. Daniel once played a young David Copperfield. 7. True. 8. True. 9. True. 10. True. 11. False. Her full name is Madonna Louise Veronica. 12. True. 13. False. There are only 12 letters. 14. False. It's the other way round. 15. True. 16. False. He left before graduating. 17. False. They're all different. 18. True. 19. True. 20. False. It first aired in 1958.

Meet Me!

CARO

Hi, I'm caroline and I'd like to show you round my room. It's where I chill out with my friends - so come on in!

This bead curtain was a Christmas gift from my auntie. It's lilac and pink to match my bedroom and it looks great hung down the side of my bed.

Practical *and* pretty - that's this great wall tidy. I love it.

I'm a kinda casual girl, so this is easily my favourite outfit - black combat pants and my Attitude top.

I love to put on music when my friends come round, or listen to my favourite CDs when I'm relaxing after school.

I'm very proud of my football trophies. I'm in a girls' football team and we are coached by my dad. He's on the bottom right of the photo.

My pride and joy - my Player of the Season trophy!

I love my groovy bed too, and like to curl up with my favourite Harry Potter books.

"What's that? A call up for England?" My auntie gave me this phone when she got a new one.

This mp3 player was my best Christmas present ever.

How d'you like my cool Narnia slippers? They match my bedroom.

My friends and I all collect soft toys, My favourites are my tigers.

I don't have many real pets, apart from a rabbit who lives in the garden and is really hard to catch, but I do have a toy hamster. He's **much** less trouble.

Thanks to all the girls. It's been great chatting to them.

PUZZLES! PUZZLES! PUZZLES!

a

b

c

d

GOOD SPORTS!

Here are four well-known sports stars pictured away from their sports. Can you name them and the sport each is famous for?

E	V	O	R	E	K	I	H
A	S	T	G	R	Y	L	E
R	E	E	S	T	B	L	G
S	D	N	K	H	E	A	N
T	H	O	A	I	B	R	G
S	E	Y	L	L	L	L	Y
I	S	O	L	O	M	I	M
M	P	N	S	H	Y	F	A

It's Wild

Solve the clues to find the names of te animals and one bird, then fit the names into the word swirl. Each word begins with the last letter of the previous word.

Fun! Fun! Fun!

Moving from square to square, up, down or diagonally, how often can you spell the word fun? It's harder than it looks.

Missing link!

Fit one of the words below into each set of brackets to make two new words or phrases.
eg horse (play) time

house hat day horse tree board

a) top ( ) box

b) card ( ) room

c) good ( ) light

d) pear ( ) house

e) clothes ( ) power

f) dog ( ) boat

TV Test!

Starting and finishing in the coloured square, make your way through the grid, finding the names of seven of the TV shows listed below. You can travel up, down and across, but not diagonally and the only letter that is used more than once is the one in the coloured square. Which TV show is not used?

Grange Hill
The Bill
Hollyoaks
EastEnders

Byker Grove
The Simpsons
Emmerdale
My Family

A gee-gee.
He never forgets.
Large striped cat from Asia.
Bugs Bunny is one.
He raced a hare in a fable.
Another name for a moose.
Australian hopper.
This bird is said to hide his head in the sand.
This 'river horse' likes wallowing in mud.
He could be red or grey, and lives in trees.
The king of the jungle.

Answers

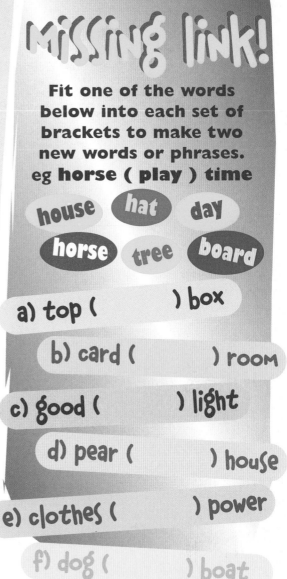

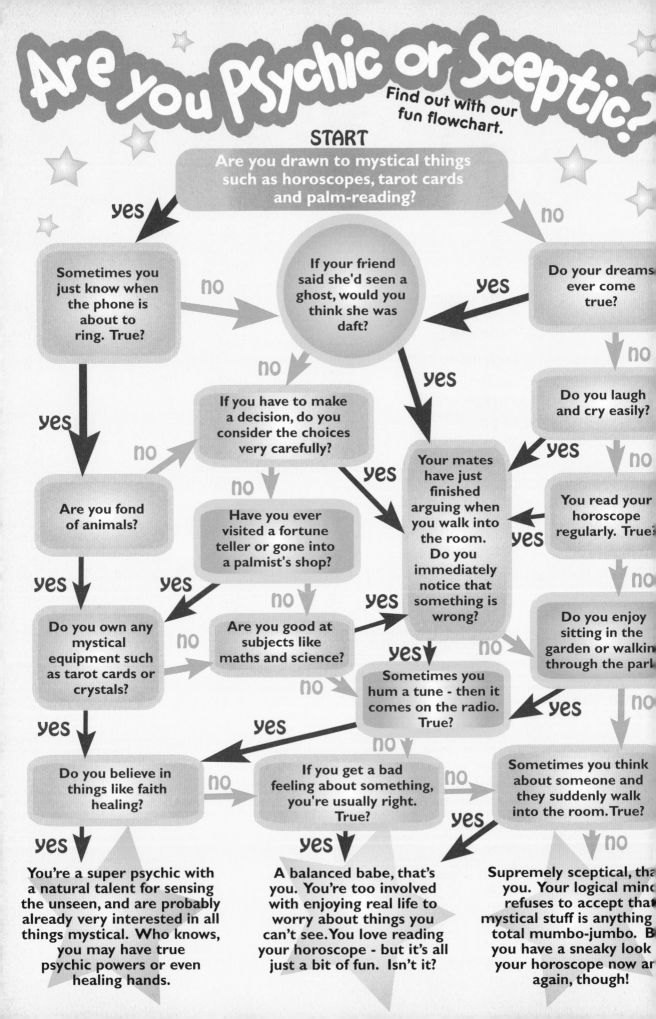

focus on...

Jennifer 2

Jennifer Lynn Lopez was born on 24th July, 1969 in South Bronx, New York City.

She is the middle of three girls, with sisters called Leslie and Lynda.

After graduating from High School, Jennifer worked in a law office during the day and as a dancer at night.

J-Lo started singing and dancing lessons when she was 5 years old.

Her big break into acting came in 1990 when she appeared in the comedy 'In Living Colour'.

Jen's mum was a teacher and her father worked with computers.

She doesn't drink alcohol.

Not everyone likes Jennifer's acting and she won a 'Worst Actress' award for her role in 'Gigli' in 2003.

She has been married three times. Her first marriage, to Ojani Noa, lasted less than a year.

Although her parents are native Spanish speakers, Jennifer isn't fluent in the language.

Her parents are both from Puerto Rico, but they didn't meet until they had moved to the United States.

Jennifer is 1.68m tall.

One of J-Lo's early role models was the Puerto Rican actress and dancer, Rita Moreno, who starred in 'West Side Story'.

Jennifer has had success as both a singer and an actress and is the first woman to have both a film, 'The Wedding Planner', and an album at number 1 in the same week.

Continued from page 96.

Rowan Lodge

Allie was sure the map she had found would lead her to an exciting find in Rowan Lodge, the old summerhouse —

I'll go first thing in the morning. Oh, I can hardly wait. I'm sure it's a birthday present to Auntie Mac from her brother, Cyril.

But, in the night, someone paid a visit —

Meanwhile, Allie was dreaming —

Lally! Wake up, Lally. Green is dangerous.

What? Who's there?

I must have been dreaming. It was as if Cyril was here in the room. And he called me Lally.

110

I wonder what he meant by 'green is dangerous'? Oh, well, I'd better get some more sleep or I'll be too tired to go hunting in the morning.

The next morning Allie slept in —

Oh, no. The map! It's gone.

She dressed quickly, then —

What are those two up to? It's a bit early for Mrs Green to be at the Grange! We usually get our own breakfast.

That's it! *That's* what Cyril meant. It's Mrs Green who is dangerous. I bet she's pinched the map and thinks it'll lead her to treasure. I must find Auntie Mac.

Allie blurted out the whole story —

. . . and now I think Mrs Green and Kelly have gone to Rowan Lodge to see what they can find. They must think it'll be valuable.

I've had my doubts about that woman. Some of Auntie's things have gone missing, even in the few days we've been here. Let's catch them red-handed.

I always wondered why Cyril didn't get me a present. I thought it was because we all disapproved of his going to the war.

The map to find it fell down the back of the drawer. It didn't show up until Kelly pulled the drawer out.

111

What did the map say, Allie?

It was strange. It gave paces, then said to open and shut the bible twice.

Yes, dearest Rilly would have put that in. Don't worry. That woman Green will never work it out.

Think, Kelly. What can it mean?

I don't know. It doesn't make sense. There's no bible here.

It makes perfect sense to me.

Miss MacDonald!

Yes, Mrs Green. The game's up.

Oi! Come back!

Let them go, Allie. I'll get the police on to them later. I'd prefer it if they weren't here when we find the gift.

113

There was a card inside, and —

She's beautiful! Only Cyril knew that I wanted a doll like this. Bless him. Oh, I wish my parents were here to see this. They thought he'd deliberately forgotten.

I know he was killed on your birthday, Auntie. I saw his name on the war memorial.

Come on, let's tidy up and get back to the house.

Who's that?

There's no one there. It must have been a trick of the light again.

Later —

I've told the police about Mrs Green. They're going to see if any of the missing valuables are in her house.

She and her mother probably half believed the story, and wanted to find the treasure for themselves.

Yeah! Mrs Green didn't like me going anywhere around the house and garden — even when Auntie Mac said I could. She was probably scared in case I found something.

I'm a bit sorry Kelly was involved. We got on really well — although she seemed to be obsessed with the story about hidden treasure.

Sleep Tight!

When you close the curtains in your bedroom and snuggle under the duvet for a nice snooze, have you ever wondered where baby animals sleep, and just what their bedrooms are like? If so, then read on.

Spiders

It's beautiful, useful - and tasty!

Unless you are lucky enough to live in a gingerbread house, can you imagine having to eat your own home? Well, that's what spiders do. Once their webs become dirty and torn lots of spiders just eat the old one and spin a new one. A baby spider doesn't have to be taught to do this as the skill comes naturally. For many spiders, webs are a combination of bedroom, kitchen and supermarket. Insects get caught in the sticky web and remain there, all ready for the spider to eat when hunger strikes.

© E Bomford / ardea.com

Meerkats

Fresh air for these young meerkats and their babysitter.

© C Haagner / ardea.com

Meerkats live in Southern Africa, in the Kalahari Desert. If a young meerkat wanted some peace and quite it would be out of luck, because these creatures live in colonies of up to forty. Their homes are underground, often up to eight feet below the surface of the ground, which means that the temperature stays constant - never too hot and never too cold. The burrows are lined with grass, which helps to keep them cosy, and there are often up to seventy entries to the burrows. The baby meerkats don't come above ground until they are at least three weeks old and then they are always carefully watched by a babysitter - who can be any of the adults in the colony. Unfortunately, although the 'bedrooms' are warm and cosy, the meerkats don't have separate toilets, so the burrows become very smelly. When this happens, the colony just builds a new burrow and moves 'house'.

Otters

This 'otter' make a good place to live.

Many animals like to live under or above ground, but some, like European otters, prefer to live by the water. They live in dens known as holts, and are particularly fond of reedbeds because the long grasses give them good cover and make them difficult to spot by other animals and humans. An individual otter can have up to thirty holts which can be built in tree roots, river banks or under rock piles. The female will chose the safest of these holts as a bedroom for her babies and usually has two or three young in a litter. The babies, who live with their mother for the first year, stay safely inside their bedroom holt for around ten weeks, then they will venture outside, returning to the bedroom to sleep and rest.

© J de Meester / ardea.com

woodpeckers

Woodpeckers are very good at making nests. They drill holes in trees, drink the sap that pours out of it, then live in the hole made inside. Once they've drilled the holes, they start 'decorating' with things like feathers, twigs, sticks, hair and fur. The adult woodpeckers will make the nest as comfortable as possible before laying their eggs, as they want the babies to be safe. Unfortunately, they also love bright shiny things, so will sometimes put coloured stones or bits of glass in the nest. These aren't always such a good idea, because baby chicks are also fascinated by the shiny things and may make themselves ill by eating them. Once the woodpeckers have left their nests, other birds and creatures often use them as shelters or even homes, so the lovely 'bedrooms' are used over and over again.

Who needs a power drill to build a house?

© D Usher / ardea.com

© J Cancalosi / ardea.com

Cute 'n' cosy, cobber!

Kangaroos

Some animals don't even have to get out of bed to eat. Baby kangaroos, called Joeys, live in their mothers' pouches for about 300 days. They suckle milk from the teats inside the pouch, and once they venture outside into the big wide world, they can still nip back for a quick drink or a nap. When a baby kangaroo is born, it is tiny and blind, but it is quite safe and warm inside its mother's pouch. If there's any danger, the mother can tighten her pouch muscles to make sure that Joey doesn't fall out. But baby kangaroos have to behave themselves, beacuse Mum can also tip them out of their warm 'bedrooms' if she likes.

Cuckoos

Okay, bird brain! Spot the cuckoo's egg in this hedge sparrow's nest.

Of all these different species, the laziest and craftiest are the cuckoos. A baby cuckoo doesn't know what kind of bedroom it may end up in, because the mother cuckoo simply lays her egg in another bird's nest. The nesting bird doesn't realize the cuckoo egg isn't her own, and she happily sits on it until it hatches. The baby cuckoo usually hatches before the other eggs, so it then empties the nest by pushing out the other eggs. Once it has its bedroom all to itself, the cuckoo chick demands the full attention of its foster parents and quickly grows - usually to many times the size of its foster parents. Then, once it's ready to fly, it's off! It's a very mean trick, but it seems to work very well for cuckoos, because they don't have all the trouble and bother of building nests and feeding young. But it really does prove that birds are not the most intelligent of creatures, doesn't it?

© J Mason / ardea.com

BEST FRIENDS!

How well do you really know your best mate? Try this fun quiz, then ask your friend to say how many answers you got right. When you've finished you can swap over. Be honest – and have fun!

1. It's your best friend's birthday and you give her a matching necklace, bracelet and ring. She has already been given two identical sets, so what would she do?
a) Smile, say thanks and then put it back in the wrapping paper.
b) Say she's already got others the same, but she really likes it!
c) Say thanks, then tell the truth and ask if she can exchange it.

2. Your aunt has offered to take you and your best friend out to a special fish and chip bar. Your best friend hates fish and chips, so does she...
a) Come along and just nibble at the gherkins and mushy peas?
b) Force herself to eat, and say, "thanks, everything is delicious"?
c) Say she's busy and can't manage?

3. Your best friend really fancies your older brother, but hasn't actually told you. Does she...
a) Always happen to arrive just as your brother comes home from school?
b) Arrange a party, and say, casually, that your brother can come along if he's free?
c) Come straight to the point and ask you if he has a girlfriend?

4. As captain of the netball team your friend has to pick the teams. You aren't really much good at netball, so how does she react?
a) She'd pick you as first reserve and try to practise with you every day in secret.
b) She'd leave you out, but say you might make the team next term.
c) She'd pick you anyway. After all, you are her best friend!

5. There are no tickets left for the school disco and your best friend really wants to go. Would she....
a) Ring the person who's in charge of the tickets, every ten minutes, in case there are any returns?

b) Try to buy a ticket from someone else by promising to lend them her iPod/Playstation/sister for a month?

c) Say she really doesn't want to go, but secretly vow to buy a ticket earlier next time?

6. **A new girl has just joined the class and wants to steal your friend. She saves a place at a table where there's no room for you. Does your best friend...**

a) Suggest you all move to another table where there's room for three?

b) Pull up an extra chair for you to squeeze in right next to her?

c) Tell the girl that she won't sit anywhere without you cos you're her best friend.

7. **You've invited your friend to a sleepover party, but her mum won't let her come because she's grounded for that week. Does she...**

a) Nag at her mother until she changes her mind?

b) Ask you to change the party to next week.

c) Accept that it's her own fault – but sulk a bit.

8. **Your best friend's parents have taken the family abroad for a few months. How would your friend keep in touch with you?**

a) Text and e-mail at least once a day.

b) Contact you by e-mail, phone or letter once a week.

c) Spend hours on the phone, checking you are okay.

9. **You come top in the maths test at school, and your best friend comes bottom. What would she be most likely to do?**

a) Ask you to help her with all her maths homework.

b) Congratulate you! Maths has always been your best subject.

c) Admit she's jealous. She'd love to be as good as you at maths.

10. **You catch chicken pox over the summer holidays, and are not allowed to see people because it's contagious. What would your best friend most probably do?**

a) Send you cards and parcels to cheer you up.

b) Ring you every evening, and tell you how much she misses you.

c) Ring you occasionally, but check with your family that you are okay as well.

Friendship rating!
Now compare answers to see how well you know your friend.

9 or 10 answers the same
Wow! There's nothing you don't know about your best friend. You must have been buddies for ages and are obviously very close. But it's sometimes good to give each other a bit of space, too, you know! You don't have to tell each other *everything* to stay good friends.

5 – 8
You know each other well – but you can still spring a few surprises now and again. You realise that everyone has a few secret thoughts that they like to keep to themselves, and just because your friend doesn't always tell you everything, it doesn't mean that she doesn't value you as a friend.

1 – 4
You like your friend – but you don't know a lot about the way she thinks, do you? That doesn't mean you won't stay friends, though, because lots of people prefer friendships where they don't share every tiny detail of what they are thinking. Sometimes is really nice to be surprised by a friend's reaction.

0
Either someone cheated and didn't give really honest answers, or you and your friend haven't known each other very long and have only been best friends for a very short time. If that's the case, then don't worry cos you've got lots of time to get to know each other better in the future.

121

122

123

124

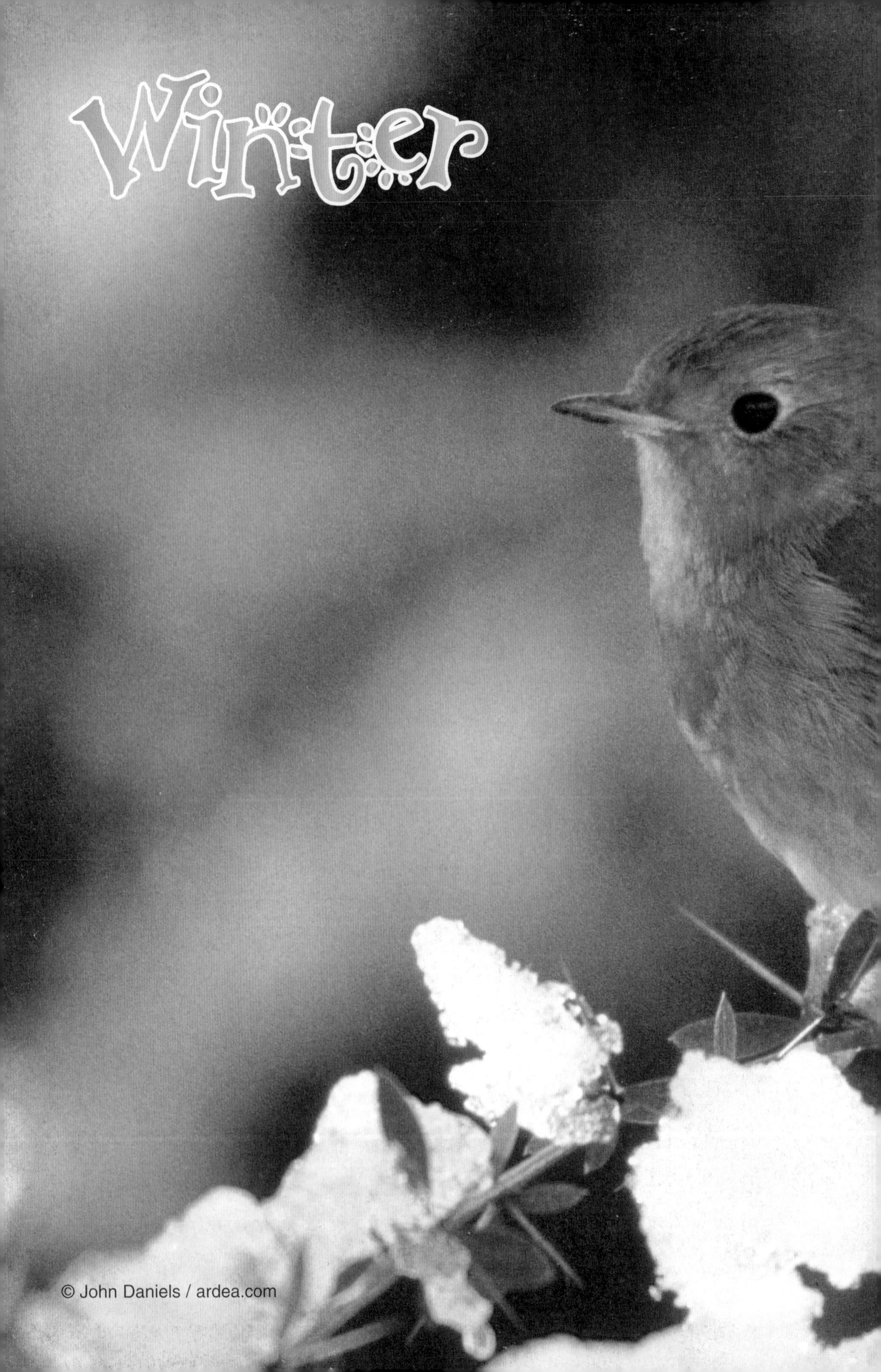
Winter